MW00366024

Library of Congress Cataloging-in-Publication Data

Powell, Richard, (date)
    Parents / words by Richard Powell; pictures by Alan Snow.
       p.   cm.—(A Child's practical guide)
    Title on cover: How to deal with parents.
    Summary: A practical guide to dealing with parents in such areas
as mealtime, riding in the car, watching television, and bedtime.
     ISBN 0-8167-2418-0 (lib. bdg.)   ISBN 0-8167-2419-9 (pbk.)
     1. Parent and child—Juvenile literature. [1. Parent and child.
2. Behavior.] I. Snow, Alan, ill. II. Title. III. Title: How to
deal with parents. IV. Series: Powell, Richard, 1957- Child's
practical guide.
     HQ755.85.P685 1992
     306.874—dc20   91-14997

Published by Watermill Press,
an imprint of Troll Associates, Inc.
Produced for Watermill Press by Joshua Morris Publishing, Inc.
in association with Treehouse Children's Books Ltd.
Illustrations copyright © 1990 Alan Snow.
Text copyright © 1990 Treehouse Children's Books Ltd.
10 9 8 7 6 5 4 3

How to Deal with
PARENTS

Words by Richard Powell
Pictures by Alan Snow

Watermill Press

Once upon a time I could never get my parents to do what I wanted. They got angry a lot, especially when . . .

I jumped on their bed . . .

I left my toys out . . .

I would *not* eat . . .

I would *not* go to bed . . .

I would *not* leave the toy store . . .

I stood in front of the television.

This often meant I had a very bad day. But now I know what to do, and we all have a great day. If you sometimes have bad days too, here are a few hints on how to make them good ones . . .

"Good morning!"

I say "good morning" to my parents . . . quietly.
Don't jump on the bed and shout:
"WAKE UP, LAZYBONES!"
It might be the start of a very bad day.

"You smell!"

Parents don't like children who don't take baths.
Neither do I.
My brother Albert never washes. Yuck!

"Brush your teeth, *now*!"

"Your teeth will rot and fall out," said Mom.
"You will get a toothache," said Dad.
"That's *worse* than having a haircut," they said.
Wow! Now I make sure I brush my teeth.

"Aren't you dressed yet?"

It's quicker to dress yourself — sometimes.
Ask Mom or Dad to help with the hard parts . . .
parents like to feel needed. It's a good idea to
ask what clothes you should wear.

"Albert, don't spit, dear."

If your parents are like my parents, they like eating. But they get frustrated if they have to stop. They get annoyed if they have to clean up a mess. They get

"Pass the milk, please."

upset if I don't eat my food. So I eat my food. Anyway, I need lots of energy because of all the playing I do, and food gives me energy.

"Where's my skateboard, Dad?"

Parents don't like toys left all over the floor.
They pick them up and put them away.
I don't know why.
It takes me ages to get them all out again.

"Look at that!"

Grownups find it very hard to play *and* drive.
So don't shout in their ear.
Don't poke them in the back.
Keep your seat belt on . . . just in case.

"I WANT!"

My brother Albert is awful in stores. I'm not.
He always wants something. So do I.
But the more he shouts "I want," the louder Dad
says "No." So I keep quiet. Sometimes I get a treat.

"Mom, mom, mom, mom, MOM!"

You know that parents talk, talk, talk, and talk.
You know they don't always listen.
But if you shout, they only talk louder.
Try saying, "Excuse me . . ." It works like magic.

"It wasn't me."

Sometimes things just go wrong. You forget for a moment what you're doing, and suddenly you're in trouble. All you can do is tell the truth.
It makes parents less mad.

"One for you, six for me."

My brother Albert gets upset if I don't share.
That makes my parents angry.
They don't like it when Albert and I fight. So I share
with Albert, and he shares with me . . . sometimes.

"Here are the first pictures of a Martian."

Parents like watching television, too.
Sometimes you should let them do what they want.
It keeps them happy. Remember, the happier parents
are, the better behaved they are.

"Be good while we're out, won't you?"

Moms and dads sometimes have to go out on their own.
You might have a baby sitter look after you.
Be nice to the baby sitter, and the baby sitter will
be nice to you. That makes moms and dads happy.

I like going to bed.
I used to cry and kick and shout
"No!" when it was time for bed.

But now I know it's nicer to share a story and
to finish the day with what makes parents happiest
of all . . .

"Ah!"

. . . a big hug.